D0366948

TOOLBOX
FOR LIFE

FOUR SKILLS YOU
NEED TO SUCCEED

TOOLBOX FOR LIFE: FOUR SKILLS YOU NEED TO SUCCEED
A Four-Session Study for Small Groups or Individuals

Copyright © 2017 Rick Warren. All rights reserved. No part of this book may be reproduced, stored in a retrieval system, or transmitted in any form, without the written permission of Purpose Driven Publishers.

Published by Purpose Driven Publishers
23182 Arroyo Vista
Rancho Santa Margarita, CA 92688

Scripture quotations noted BSB are from The Holy Bible, Berean Study Bible, BSB. Copyright ©2016 by Bible Hub. Used by permission. All rights reserved worldwide.

Scripture quotations noted CEV are from The Contemporary English Version. Copyright © 1991, 1992, 1995 by American Bible Society. Used by permission.

Scripture quotations noted ESV are from The Holy Bible, English Standard Version®, ESV®, Copyright © 2001 by Crossway, a publishing ministry of Good News Publishers. Used by permission. All rights reserved.

Scripture quotations noted GNT are from the Good News Translation in Today's English Version—Second Edition. Copyright © 1992 by American Bible Society. Used by permission.

Scripture quotations noted GW are from God's Word®. Copyright © 1995 God's Word to the Nations. Used by permission of Baker Publishing Group. All rights reserved

Scripture quotations noted ICB are from the The Holy Bible, International Children's Bible® Copyright© 1986, 1988, 1999, 2015 by Tommy Nelson™, a division of Thomas Nelson. Used by permission.

Scripture quotations noted KNOX are taken from the KNOX BIBLE, The Holy Bible: A Translation From the Latin Vulgate in the Light of the Hebrew and Greek Originals by Monsignor Ronald Knox. Copyright© 1954 Westminster Diocese.

Scripture quotations noted NCV are from the New Century Version®. Copyright © 2005 by Thomas Nelson. Used by permission. All rights reserved.

Scripture quotations noted NIV are from The Holy Bible, New International Version®, NIV®. Copyright © 1973, 1978, 1984, 2011 by Biblica, Inc.® Used by permission of Zondervan. All rights reserved worldwide. The "NIV" and "New International Version" are trademarks registered in the United States Patent and Trademark Office by Biblica, Inc.™

Scripture quotations noted NLT are from The Holy Bible, New Living Translation. Copyright© 1996, 2004, 2007, 2013, 2015 by Tyndale House Publishers, Inc., Wheaton, Illinois, 60189. All rights reserved.

Scripture quotations noted The Message are from The Message. Copyright © by Eugene H. Peterson, 1993, 1994, 1995, 1996, 2000, 2001, 2002. Used by permission of NavPress Publishing Group. All rights reserved. Represented by Tyndale House Publishers, Inc.

Scripture quotations noted TLB are from The Living Bible. Copyright © 1971. Used by permission of Tyndale House Publishers, Wheaton, IL 60189. All rights reserved.

Scripture quotations noted WEB are from the World English Bible, a public domain (no copyright) modern English translation of the Holy Bible.

ISBN: 978-1-4228-0418-6

Printed and bound in the United States of America.

TABLE OF CONTENTS

HOW TO USE THIS VIDEO CURRICULUM

Here is a brief explanation of the features of this study guide.

CHECKING IN:

You will open each meeting with an opportunity for everyone to check in with each other about how you are doing with the weekly assignments. Accountability is a key to success in this study!

KEY VERSE:

Each week you will find a key verse or Scripture passage for your group to read together. If someone in the group has a different translation, ask them to read it aloud so the group can get a deeper perspective of the meaning of the passage.

VIDEO LESSON:

There is a video lesson for the group to watch together each week. Fill in the blanks in the lesson outlines as you watch the video, and be sure to refer back to these outlines during your discussion time.

DISCOVERY QUESTIONS:

Each video segment is complemented by several questions for group discussion. Please don't feel pressured to discuss every single question. There is no reason to rush through the answers. Give everyone ample opportunity to share their thoughts. If you don't get through all of the discussion questions, that's okay.

PUTTING IT INTO PRACTICE:

This is where the rubber meets the road. We don't want to be just hearers of the Word. We also need to be doers of the Word (James 1:22). These assignments are application exercises that will help you put into practice the truths you have discussed in the lesson.

PRAYER DIRECTION:

At the end of each session you will find suggestions for your group prayer time. Praying together is one of the greatest privileges of small group life. Please don't take it for granted.

A TIP FOR THE HOST

The study guide material is meant to be your servant, not your master. The point is not to race through the sessions; the point is to take time to let God work in your lives. Nor is it necessary to "go around the circle" before you move on to the next question. Give people the freedom to speak, but don't insist on it. Your group will enjoy deeper, more open sharing and discussion if people don't feel pressured to speak up.

SESSION 1:
IGNORING THE NAYSAYERS

CHECKING IN:

If this is your first time to meet as a group, or if you have any new group members, be sure to introduce yourselves. Encourage people to share what they are hoping to learn from this study.

KEY VERSE:

If the ax is dull and its edge unsharpened,
*more strength is needed, but **skill** will bring success.*
ECCLESIASTES 10:10 (NIV, EMPHASIS ADDED)

DEALING WITH NAYSAYERS

NAYSAYER (from Webster's Dictionary): a person who says something won't work or isn't possible; a cynic who habitually expresses pessimistic views.

FOUR NAYSAYERS DAVID FACED
BEFORE GOLIATH

1.) _____ held him back.

Now David was the son of a man named Jesse . . . and he had eight sons.
David was the youngest son. David's three oldest brothers stayed with
Saul's army, but David went back and forth so he could help his father
with the sheep in Bethlehem.
1 SAMUEL 17:12, 14-15 (NLT)

┌── **BARRIERS TO SUCCESS:** ──┐
│ _____ │
└─────────────────────────────┘

2.) _____ was afraid.

┌── **BARRIERS TO SUCCESS:** ──┐
│ _____ │
└─────────────────────────────┘

Goliath stood and shouted a taunt across to the Israelites. "Why are you all
coming out to fight?" he called. "I am the Philistine champion, but you are only
the servants of Saul. Choose one man to come down here and fight me! If he kills
me, then we will be your slaves. But if I kill him, you will be our slaves! I defy the
armies of Israel today! Send me a man who will fight me!" When Saul and the
Israelites heard this, they were terrified and deeply shaken.
1 SAMUEL 17:8-11 (NLT)

CONVENTIONAL WISDOM IS OFTEN WRONG.

PUBLIC OPINION IS OFTEN WRONG.

MAJORITY DOESN'T MAKE SOMETHING RIGHT.

3.) _____ questioned his motives.

┌─── **BARRIERS TO SUCCESS:** ───┐
│ _____ │
└───────────────────────────────┘

*David talked to some others standing there to verify the report. "What will a
man get for killing this Philistine and ending his insults to Israel?" . . .
But when David's oldest brother, Eliab, heard David talking like that, he was
angry. "What are you doing around here, anyway?" he demanded. "What about
the sheep you're supposed to be taking care of? I know what a cocky brat you are;
you just want to see the battle!" "What have I done now?" David replied.
I was only asking a question!"*
1 SAMUEL 17:26-29 (TLB)

4.) _____ doubted his ability.

┌─── **BARRIERS TO SUCCESS:** ───┐
│ _____ │
└───────────────────────────────┘

*"Don't worry about a thing," David told him. "I'll take care of this Philistine!"
"Don't be ridiculous!" Saul replied. "How can a kid like you fight with a man
like him? You are only a boy, and he has been in the army since he was a boy!"*
1 SAMUEL 17:32-33 (TLB)

HOW TO DEFEAT THE NAYSAYERS
IN YOUR LIFE

1.) Remember they are _____!

The fear of human opinion disables; trusting in God protects you from that.
PROVERBS 29:25 (THE MESSAGE)

It is dangerous to be concerned with what others think of you.
PROVERBS 29:25 (GNT)

What other people think of you is none of your business.

Do not fear anything except the Lord Almighty.
He alone is the Holy One. If you fear him, you need fear nothing else.
ISAIAH 8:13 (NLT)

2.) Don't get _____!

Motivated reasoning is based on emotion, not logic.

Don't be intimidated. Eventually everything is going to be out in the open,
and everyone will know how things really are.
MATTHEW 10:26 (THE MESSAGE)

3.) Never _____!

It is foolish to speak scornfully of others. If you are smart, you will keep quiet.
PROVERBS 11:12 (GNT)

When they hurled their insults at Jesus, he did not retaliate; when he suffered,
he made no threats. Instead, he entrusted himself to him who judges justly.
1 PETER 2:23 (NIV)

I am most like Jesus when I stay silent under attack.

4.) Stay focused on _____ and _____!

David was now in great danger because all his men were very bitter . . . and they
began to talk of stoning him. But David found strength in the Lord his God.
1 SAMUEL 30:6 (NLT)

The Lord is for me, so I will not be afraid. What can mere mortals do to me?
PSALM 118:6 (NLT)

You don't need anybody else's approval to be happy.

Show me how much you love me, Lord, and save me according to your promise.
Then I can answer those who insult me because I trust in your word.
PSALM 119:41-42 (GNT)

I've banked your promises in the vault of my heart.
PSALM 119:11 (THE MESSAGE)

DISCOVERY QUESTIONS:

1. Has there been someone who has acted as a naysayer in your life? How did you deal with the situation? How would you deal with it now?

2. Of the *Four Barriers to Success* (delay, discouragement, disapproval, and doubt), which one have you encountered most recently? How would God want you to respond to that barrier?

3. Pastor Rick taught that we are most like Jesus when we stay silent under attack. Share an example of a time you chose to stay silent under attack. How did God bless your decision?

PUTTING IT INTO PRACTICE:

In this week's lesson, we learned that we don't need anyone else's approval to be happy.

Whose approval are you still seeking? How would it change your life if you could let go of your desire to seek that person's approval?

_____

_____

This week, think of one person whose approval you still seek. Talk to God about it and practice trusting him.

_____

PRAYER DIRECTION:

Spend some time silently praying for the naysayers in your life. Ask God to give you compassion for them and to help you understand why they may be a naysayer in your life.

Ask God to help discern if someone is a naysayer, or if that person is actually offering you biblical advice.

Ask God to give you opportunities this week to trust what he says about you more than you trust what the naysayers say about you.

SESSION 2:
KNOWING WHAT MATTERS MOST

CHECKING IN:

Last week we looked at four ways to defeat the naysayers in your life.
How was the lesson helpful to you this week?

KEY VERSE:

"Everything is permissible for me," but not everything is beneficial.
1 CORINTHIANS 6:12 (BSB)

EVERY SINGLE TIME YOU MAKE A DECISION, YOU'RE BASING IT ON UNSPOKEN VALUES.

MY VALUES DETERMINE:

- MY STRESS
- MY SUCCESS
- MY SALVATION

FOUR QUESTIONS THAT WILL DETERMINE YOUR VALUES AND YOUR DESTINY

1.) Who is going to be _____?

┌─ **WHERE DO I GET MY VALUES:** ─┐

└─────────────────────┘

The human mind is the most deceitful of all things.
It is incurable. No one can understand how deceitful it really is.
JEREMIAH 17:9 (GW)

DECEITFUL (from Webster's Dictionary): to mislead in the
wrong direction.

My perceptions say more about _____ **than** _____.

There is a way which seems right to a man, but in the end it leads to death.
PROVERBS 16:25 (WEB)

┌─ **WHERE DO I GET MY VALUES:** ─┐

└─────────────────────┘

Don't love the world and what it offers. Those who love the world don't have
the Father's love in them. Not everything that the world offers—
physical gratification, greed, and extravagant lifestyles—
comes from the Father. It comes from the world.
1 JOHN 2:15-16 (GW)

THE WORLD'S VALUES

- **LOOKING GOOD (BEAUTY)**

- **FEELING GOOD (PLEASURE)**

- **HAVING THE GOODS (MATERIALISM)**

⌐ WHERE DO I GET MY VALUES: ⌐

_____

If you continue in My word . . . Then you will know the truth,
and the truth will set you free.
JOHN 8:31-32 (BSB)

2.) What is going to _____?

We don't change when we see the light, we change when we feel the heat.

The world is passing away along with its desires,
but whoever does the will of God remains forever.
1 JOHN 2:17 (BSB)

Temptation is always a dilemma between now or later.

For we fix our attention, not on things that are seen,
but on things that are unseen. What can be seen lasts only
for a time, but what cannot be seen lasts forever.
2 CORINTHIANS 4:18 (GNT)

3.) Will I choose what's _____ or what's _____?

LIVING BY YOUR VALUES IS CALLED

- _____

- _____

- _____

Will I live what I claim to believe?

4.) Is it worth _____?

Anytime you say yes to something, you're saying no to something else.

> *"What profit is there if you gain the whole world—and lose eternal life?*
> *What can be compared with the value of eternal life?"*
> MATTHEW 16:26 (TLB)

> *"What kind of deal is it to get everything you want but lose yourself?*
> *What could you ever trade your soul for?"*
> MATTHEW 16:26 (THE MESSAGE)

> *Jesus said . . . "The things that are considered great value by people*
> *are worth nothing in God's sight."*
> LUKE 16:15 (GNT)

> *Jesus said, "Many people who seem to be important now*
> *will be the least important then."*
> MARK 10:31 (TLB)

Every temptation is always a choice between God or me.

> *I once thought all these things were so very important, but now I consider them*
> *worthless because of what Christ has done. Yes, everything else is worthless*
> *when compared with the priceless gain of knowing Christ Jesus my Lord. I have*
> *discarded everything else, counting it all as garbage, so that I may have Christ.*
> PHILIPPIANS 3:7-8 (NLT)

Success is living by the values that God will reward someday.

DISCOVERY QUESTIONS:

1. This week's session is based around God's values. Share with your group the value that has had the greatest impact on your spiritual life.

2. Which world value do you struggle with the most? What have you learned in this lesson that will help you turn things around?

3. Can you think of a time you chose what was **easy** versus what was **best**? What was the cost of that decision, and how did it change the way you handled future choices?

PUTTING IT INTO PRACTICE:

Pastor Rick taught that every temptation is basically just a choice between God or me.

Over the next week, you will face, temptation. Take some time to consider what you might face and think about how you can intentionally choose God's path over your own.

_____

_____

PRAYER DIRECTION:

As you pray together, ask God to give you the wisdom to embrace his values, so your decisions are a reflection of his Word. Ask God to reveal any area of your life where you're not aligned with his values.

Pray for clarity and conviction so you can live what you believe. Ask God to give you the courage to say yes to only the best, and let go of the rest.

Finally, ask God to guide and empower you as you encounter temptations this week.

SESSION 3:
MAXIMIZING YOUR STRENGTHS

CHECKING IN:

Last week we talked about temptations and what the Bible says about how we should handle them. What temptations did you experience this past week? How did what you learned last session help you when you faced temptation?

KEY VERSE:

"Before I shaped you in the womb, I knew all about you.
Before you saw the light of day, I had holy plans for you."
JEREMIAH 1:5 (THE MESSAGE)

The 5 Elements God Uses to "SHAPE" Your Life

S – Spiritual Gifts

H – Heart

A – Abilities

P – Personality

E - Experiences

You made my whole being; you formed me in my mother's body.
I praise you because you made me in an amazing and wonderful way . . .
You saw my bones being formed as I took shape in my mother's body.
When I was put together there, you saw my body as it was formed.
All the days planned for me were written in your book before
I was one day old.
PSALM 139:13-16 (NCV)

GOD WAS:

_____ IN MY BIRTH

HOW DO I MAXIMIZE MY GOD-GIVEN SHAPE?

1.) _____ my **SHAPE**

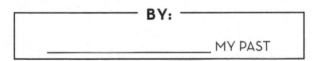

BY:

_____ MY PAST

You have experienced many things. Were all those experiences wasted?
GALATIANS 3:4 (ICB)

Everyone should examine his own conduct; then he will be able to
take the measure of his own worth; with no need to compare himself with others.
GALATIANS 6:4 (KNOX)

BY:

_____ WITH DIFFERENT TASKS

2.) _____ my SHAPE

BARRIERS TO FULFILLING MY SHAPE:
_____ AND _____

Who do you think you are to talk back to God like that? Can an object
that was made say to its maker, "Why did you make me like this?"
A potter has the right to do whatever he wants with his clay.
ROMANS 9:20-21 (GW)

Each one should retain the place in life that the Lord assigned to him
and to which God has called him.
1 CORINTHIANS 7:17 (NIV)

So I was afraid, and I went and hid your talent in the ground.
MATTHEW 25:25 (ESV)

WHY MUST I MAXIMIZE MY SHAPE?
BECAUSE I'M _____ TO MY CREATOR

From where he sits he overlooks all us earth-dwellers.
He has shaped each person in turn; now he watches everything we do.
PSALM 33:14-15 (THE MESSAGE)

Offer the parts of your body to God to be used in doing good.
ROMANS 6:13 (NCV)

DISCOVERY QUESTIONS:

1. In what ways has comparing yourself to others impacted your life? Where in your life do you tend to conform to the world's standards? What does the Bible say about comparing and conforming?

2. In the parable of the talents, Jesus warns us not to hide the gifts God has given us. Faithful living is using your gifts well. Is there anything you are good at or anything you've always longed to try that you've kept hidden from the world? What's holding you back?

3. Is there a gift or interest that is part of your SHAPE that you're no longer using? What might happen if you started to share this part of your SHAPE again?

PUTTING IT INTO PRACTICE:

Take some time this week to examine your past and experiment with one or two different tasks, and see if God begins to lead you closer to your SHAPE.

If you've already discovered your personal SHAPE, do you feel like you have maximized your SHAPE to its greatest potential? What steps could you take this week to move toward maximizing God's investment in you?

_____

_____

_____

PRAYER DIRECTION:

As you pray together, ask God to help you discover, accept, and maximize your SHAPE.

Ask God to help you fully examine your past so you can uncover any gifts that may have become dormant.

Pray for the courage to experiment and explore some new ways of sharing your talents.

SESSION 4:
LEARNING TO BE BOTH FAST AND SLOW

CHECKING IN:

Take some time to share with the group what you discovered
last week about your SHAPE.

KEY VERSE:

There is a right time and a right way to do everything,
but we know so little!

ECCLESIASTES 8:6 (GNT)

WHEN TO MOVE FAST

***Run** hard and fast in the faith.*
1 TIMOTHY 6:12 (THE MESSAGE, EMPHASIS ADDED)

***Run** in such a way as to get the prize.*
1 CORINTHIANS 9:24 (NIV, EMPHASIS ADDED)

*I **run** straight to the goal with purpose in every step.*
1 CORINTHIANS 9:26 (TLB, EMPHASIS ADDED)

*I **run** to win!*
PHILIPPIANS 3:12 (GW, EMPHASIS ADDED)

1.) When God tells me _____.

Jesus said to them, "Come follow me."
So Simon and Andrew immediately left their nets and followed him.
MARK 1:17-18 (NCV)

Without delay I hurry to obey your commands.
PSALM 119:60 (GNT)

2.) When I need to ask or offer _____.

"If you enter your place of worship and, about to make an offering,
you suddenly remember a grudge a friend has against you,
abandon your offering, leave immediately, go to this friend and
make things right. Then and only then, come back and
work things out with God."
MATTHEW 5:23-24 (THE MESSAGE)

3.) When I feel _____.

Run away from all evil things.
1 TIMOTHY 6:11 (NLT)

Run away from the worship of idols.
1 CORINTHIANS 10:14 (NCV)

Run away from sexual sin.
1 CORINTHIANS 6:18 (NCV)

4.) When I've made a _____.

When you make a promise to God, keep it as quickly as possible.
He has no use for a fool. Do what you promise to do.
ECCLESIASTES 5:4 (GNT)

5.) When I have the opportunity _____.

Do not withhold good from those who deserve it,
while it is in your power to act.
PROVERBS 3:27 (NIV)

If you wait for perfect conditions,
you will never get anything done.
ECCLESIASTES 11:4 (NLT)

"All of us must quickly carry out the tasks assigned us
by the one who sent me, for there is little time left
before the night falls and all work comes to an end."
JOHN 9:4 (TLB)

6.) When God offers me _____.

God is ready to help you right now. Today is the day of salvation.
2 CORINTHIANS 6:2 (NLT)

WHEN TO MOVE SLOW

It's smart to be patient.
PROVERBS 14:29 (CEV)

1.) When I don't have _____.

Zeal without knowledge is not good;
a person who moves too quickly may go the wrong way.
PROVERBS 19:2 (NLT)

What a shame—yes, how stupid!—
to decide before knowing the facts!
PROVERBS 18:13 (TLB)

2.) When I'm _____ **or** _____.

Everyone should be quick to listen, slow to speak
and slow to become angry.
JAMES 1:19 (NIV)

Whoever is slow to anger has great understanding,
but people with quick tempers show their foolishness.
PROVERBS 14:29 (ESV/NCV)

The godly think before speaking.
PROVERBS 15:28 (NLT)

Losing your temper causes a lot of trouble,
but staying calm settles arguments.
PROVERBS 15:18 (CEV)

3.) When making a _____.

Wicked people bluff their way [through life],
but God's people think before they take a step.
PROVERBS 21:29 (CEV)

Ponder the path of your feet; then all your ways will be sure.
PROVERBS 4:26 (ESV)

You can't "ponder" fast.

> *Sensible people will see trouble coming and avoid it,*
> *but an unthinking person will walk right into it and regret it later.*
> PROVERBS 22:3 (GNT)

4.) When waiting for a seed I've planted _____.

> *For everything there is a season, a time for every activity under heaven . . .*
> *A time to plant and a time to harvest . . .*
> *a time to scatter. . . and a time to gather.*
> ECCLESIASTES 3:1-5 (NLT)

> *God says, "At the time I have decided, my words will come true.*
> *You can trust what I say about the future. It may take a long time,*
> *but keep on waiting—it will happen!"*
> HABAKKUK 2:3 (CEV)

> *May he [God] keep us centered and devoted to him,*
> *following the life path he has cleared, watching the signposts,*
> *and walking at the pace and rhythms he laid down for our ancestors.*
> 1 KINGS 8:58 (THE MESSAGE)

DISCOVERY QUESTIONS:

1. Think about a recent temptation you faced. How fast did you flee from it? How would you rate your response time?

2. Share an example of a time you had a chance to do good. Did you act immediately? If so, what did you see God do as a result of your quick action? Did you delay? If so, what stopped you, and how might you handle it differently next time?

3. James 1:19 teaches that we should be quick to listen, slow to speak, and slow to become angry. How have you seen God work in a situation as you followed that guidance? What's happened when you didn't?

PUTTING IT INTO PRACTICE:

What do you feel God nudging you toward doing? It may be to have a daily quiet time, invite a friend to church, or start serving in a ministry. This week, make a promise to God and take action.

_____

_____

PRAYER DIRECTION:

As you pray together, ask God to reveal any areas in your life where you've been moving too fast or too slow.

Give those areas to God and ask him for the wisdom to rest in his timing. Ask him to help you discern when to move quickly in obedience and when to be equally obedient in patience.

SMALL GROUP
RESOURCES

HELP FOR HOSTS

TOP 10 IDEAS FOR NEW HOSTS

CONGRATULATIONS! As the host of your small group, you have responded to the call to help shepherd Jesus' flock. Few other tasks in the family of God surpass the contribution you will be making. As you prepare to facilitate your group, whether it is one session or the entire series, here are a few thoughts to keep in mind.

Remember you are not alone. God knows everything about you, and he knew you would be asked to facilitate your group. Even though you may not feel ready, this is common for all good hosts. God promises, *"I will never leave you; I will never abandon you"* (Hebrews 13:5 GNT). Whether you are facilitating for one evening, several weeks, or a lifetime, you will be blessed as you serve.

1. **DON'T TRY TO DO IT ALONE.** Pray right now for God to help you build a healthy team. If you can enlist a co-host to help you shepherd the group, you will find your experience much richer. This is your chance to involve as many people as you can in building a healthy group. All you have to do is ask people to help. You'll be surprised at the response.

2. **BE FRIENDLY AND BE YOURSELF.** God wants to use your unique gifts and temperament. Be sure to greet people at the door with a big smile . . . this can set the mood for the whole gathering. Remember, they are taking as big a step to show up at your house as you are to host a small group! Don't try to do things exactly like another host; do them in a way that fits you. Admit when you don't have an answer and apologize when you make a mistake. Your group will love you for it and you'll sleep better at night.

3. **PREPARE FOR YOUR MEETING AHEAD OF TIME.** Review the session and write down your responses to each question. Pay special attention to the **Putting It Into Practice** exercises that ask group members to do something other than engage in discussion. These exercises will help your group live what the Bible teaches, not just talk about it.

4. **PRAY FOR YOUR GROUP MEMBERS BY NAME.** Before you begin your session, take a few moments and pray for each member by name. You may want to review the Small Group Prayer and Praise Report at least once a week. Ask God to use your time together to touch the heart of each person in your group. Expect God to lead you to whomever he wants you to encourage or challenge in a special way. If you listen, God will surely lead.

5. **WHEN YOU ASK A QUESTION, BE PATIENT.** Someone will eventually respond. Sometimes people need a moment or two of silence to think about the question. If silence doesn't bother you, it won't bother anyone else. After someone responds, affirm the response with a simple "thanks" or "great answer." Then ask, "How about somebody else?" or "Would someone who hasn't shared like to add anything?" Be sensitive to new people or reluctant members who aren't ready to say, pray, or do anything. If you give them a safe setting, they will blossom over time. If someone in your group is a wallflower who sits silently through every session, consider talking to them privately and encouraging them to participate. Let them know how important they are to you—that they are loved and appreciated, and that the group would value their input. Remember, still water often runs deep.

6. **PROVIDE TRANSITIONS BETWEEN QUESTIONS.** Ask if anyone would like to read the paragraph or Bible passage. Don't call on anyone, but ask for a volunteer, and then be patient until someone begins. Be sure to thank the person who reads aloud.

7. **BREAK INTO SMALLER GROUPS OCCASIONALLY.** With a greater opportunity to talk in a small circle, people will connect more with the study, apply more quickly what they're learning, and ultimately get more out of their small group experience. A small circle also encourages a quiet person to participate and tends to minimize the effects of a more vocal or dominant member.

8. **SMALL CIRCLES ARE ALSO HELPFUL DURING PRAYER TIME.** People who are unaccustomed to praying aloud will feel more comfortable trying it with just two or three others. Also, prayer requests won't take as much time, so circles will have more time to actually pray. When you gather back with the whole group, you can have one person from each circle briefly update everyone on the prayer requests from their subgroups. The other great aspect of subgrouping is that it fosters leadership development. As you ask people in the group to facilitate discussion or to lead a prayer circle, it gives them a small leadership step that can build their confidence.

9. **ROTATE FACILITATORS OCCASIONALLY.** You may be perfectly capable of hosting each time, but you will help others grow in their faith and gifts if you give them opportunities to host the group.

10. **ONE FINAL CHALLENGE (FOR NEW OR FIRST-TIME HOSTS).** Before your first opportunity to lead, read each of the six passages listed on the next page as a devotional exercise to help prepare you with a shepherd's heart.

"When he saw the crowds, he had compassion on them, because they were harassed and helpless, like sheep without a shepherd. Then he said to his disciples, 'The harvest is plentiful but the workers are few. Ask the Lord of the harvest, therefore, to send out workers into his harvest field.'
MATTHEW 9:36–38 (NIV)

"I am the good shepherd; I know my sheep and my sheep know me— just as the Father knows me and I know the Father— and I lay down my life for the sheep."
JOHN 10:14–15 (NIV)

"Be shepherds of God's flock that is under your care, watching over them—not because you must, but because you are willing, as God wants you to be; not pursuing dishonest gain, but eager to serve; not lording it over those entrusted to you, but being examples to the flock. And when the Chief Shepherd appears, you will receive the crown of glory that will never fade away."
1 PETER 5:2–4 (NIV)

"Therefore if you have any encouragement from being united with Christ, if any comfort from his love, if any common sharing in the Spirit, if any tenderness and compassion, then make my joy complete by being like minded, having the same love, being one in spirit and of one mind. Do nothing out of selfish ambition or vain conceit. Rather, in humility value others above yourselves, not looking to your own interests but each of you to the interests of the others. In your relationships with one another, have the same mindset as Christ Jesus."
PHILIPPIANS 2:1–5 (NIV)

"Let us hold unswervingly to the hope we profess, for he who promised is faithful. And let us consider how we may spur one another on toward love and good deeds, not giving up meeting together, as some are in the habit of doing, but encouraging one another—and all the more as you see the Day approaching."
HEBREWS 10:23–25 (NIV)

"But we were very gentle with you, like a mother caring for her little children. Because we loved you, we were happy to share not only God's Good News with you, but even our own lives. You had become so dear to us! . . . You know that we treated each of you as a father treats his own children. We encouraged you, we urged you, and we insisted that you live good lives for God, who calls you to his glorious kingdom."
1 THESSALONIANS 2:7–8, 11–12 (NIV)

FREQUENTLY ASKED QUESTIONS

HOW LONG WILL THIS GROUP MEET?

This study is four sessions long. We encourage your group to add a session for a celebration. In your final session, each group member may decide if he or she desires to continue on for another study. At that time you may also want to do some informal evaluation, discuss your group guidelines, and decide which study you want to do next. We recommend you visit our website at **PastorRick.com** for more video-based small group studies.

WHO IS THE HOST?

The host is the person who coordinates and facilitates your group meetings. In addition to a host, we encourage you to select one or more group members to lead your group discussions. Several other responsibilities can be rotated, including refreshments, prayer requests, worship, or keeping up with those who miss a meeting. Shared ownership in the group helps everybody grow.

WHERE DO WE FIND NEW GROUP MEMBERS?

Recruiting new members can be a challenge for groups, especially new groups with just a few people, or existing groups that lose a few people along the way. We encourage you to use the Circles of Life diagram on page 50 of this study guide to brainstorm a list of people from your workplace, church, school, neighborhood, family, and so on. Then pray for the people on each member's list. Allow each member to invite several people from their list. Some groups fear that newcomers will interrupt the intimacy that members have built over time. However, groups that welcome newcomers generally gain strength with the infusion of new blood. Remember, the next person you add just might become a friend for eternity. Logistically, groups find different ways to add members. Some groups remain permanently open, while others choose to open periodically, such as at the beginning or end of a study. If your group becomes too large for easy, face-to-face conversations, you can subgroup, forming a second discussion group in another room.

HOW DO WE HANDLE THE CHILDCARE NEEDS IN OUR GROUP?

Childcare needs must be handled very carefully. This is a sensitive issue. We suggest you seek creative solutions as a group. One common solution is to have the adults meet in the living room and share the cost of a babysitter (or two) who can be with the kids in another part of the house.

Another popular option is to have one home for the kids and a second home (close by) for the adults. If desired, the adults could rotate the responsibility of providing a lesson for the kids. This last option is great with school-age kids and can be a huge blessing to families.

CIRCLES OF LIFE

SMALL GROUP CONNECTIONS

Discover Who You Can Connect in Community Use the chart on the following page to help carry out one of the values in the Group Guidelines, to "Welcome Newcomers."

FOLLOW THIS SIMPLE THREE-STEP PROCESS:

1. List one or two people in each circle.

2. Prayerfully select one person or couple from your list and tell your group about them.

3. Give them a call and invite them to your next meeting. Over 50 percent of those invited to a small group say, "Yes!"

CIRCLES OF LIFE

FAMILY
(immediate or extended)

_____

_____

FELLOWSHIP
(church relationships)

_____

_____

FRIENDS
(neighbors, kids, sports, school, etc.)

_____

_____

FUN
(gym, hobbies, hangouts)

_____

_____

FACTORY/ FIRM
(work, professional arena)

_____

_____

GROUP GUIDELINES

It's a good idea for every group to put words to their shared values, expectations, and commitments. Such guidelines will help you avoid unspoken agendas and unmet expectations. We recommend you discuss your guidelines during Session 1 in order to lay the foundation for a healthy group experience. Feel free to modify anything that does not work for your group.

WE AGREE TO THE FOLLOWING VALUES:

CLEAR PURPOSE
To grow healthy spiritual lives by building a healthy small group community

GROUP ATTENDANCE
To give priority to the group meeting (call if I am absent or late)

SAFE ENVIRONMENT
To create a safe place where people can be heard and feel loved (no quick answers, snap judgments, or simple fixes)

BE CONFIDENTIAL
To keep anything that is shared strictly confidential and within the group

CONFLICT RESOLUTION	To avoid gossip and to immediately resolve any concerns by following the principles of Matthew 18:15–17.
SPIRITUAL HEALTH	To give group members permission to speak into my life and help me live a healthy, balanced spiritual life that is pleasing to God.
LIMIT OUR FREEDOM	To limit our freedom by not serving or consuming alcohol during small group meetings or events so as to avoid causing a weaker brother or sister to stumble (1 Corinthians 8:1–13; Romans 14:19–21).
WELCOME NEWCOMERS	To invite friends who might benefit from this study and warmly welcome newcomers.
BUILDING RELATIONSHIPS	To get to know the other members of the group and pray for them regularly.
OTHER	_____ _____ _____

WE HAVE ALSO DISCUSSED AND AGREE ON THE FOLLOWING ITEMS:

CHILDCARE   _____

STARTING TIME   _____

ENDING TIME   _____

If you haven't already done so, take a few minutes to fill out the Small Group Calendar on page 57.

SMALL GROUP PRAYER AND PRAISE REPORT

This is a place where you can write each other's requests for prayer. You can also make a note when God answers a prayer. Pray for each other's requests. If you're new to group prayer, it's okay to pray silently or to pray by using just one sentence:

"God, please help _____ to _____."

DATE/PERSON	PRAYER REQUEST	PRAISE REPORT

DATE/PERSON	PRAYER REQUEST	PRAISE REPORT

DATE/PERSON	PRAYER REQUEST	PRAISE REPORT

DATE/PERSON	PRAYER REQUEST	PRAISE REPORT

TOOLBOX FOR LIFE

SMALL GROUP CALENDAR

Healthy groups share responsibilities and group ownership. It might take some time for this to develop. Shared ownership ensures that responsibility for the group doesn't fall to one person. Use the calendar to keep track of social events, mission projects, birthdays, or days off. Complete this calendar at your first or second meeting. Planning ahead will increase attendance and shared ownership.

DATE	LESSON	LOCATION	FACILITATOR	SNACK OR MEAL
	Session 1			
	Session 2			
	Session 3			
	Session 4			
	CELEBRATION			

ANSWER KEY

SESSION 1: IGNORING THE NAYSAYERS

FOUR NAYSAYERS DAVID FACED BEFORE GOLIATH:

1.) __HIS DAD__ held him back.

> BARRIERS TO SUCCESS:
> **DELAY**

2.) __EVERYONE ELSE__ was afraid.

> BARRIERS TO SUCCESS:
> **DISCOURAGEMENT**

3.) __**HIS BROTHER**__ questioned his motives.

┌─── BARRIERS TO SUCCESS: ───┐

DISAPPROVAL
───────────────────────

4.) __**THE EXPERTS**__ doubted his ability.

┌─── BARRIERS TO SUCCESS: ───┐

DOUBT
───────────────────────

HOW TO DEFEAT THE NAYSAYERS IN YOUR LIFE:

1.) Remember they are __**NOT GOD**__!

2.) Don't get __**DISTRACTED**__!

3.) Never __**ATTACK BACK**__!

4.) Stay focused on __**GOD**__ and __**HIS PROMISES**__!

SESSION 2: KNOWING WHAT MATTERS MOST

1.) Who is going to be __**MY AUTHORITY**__?

> ## WHERE DO I GET MY VALUES:
> ### MYSELF

My perceptions say more about __**ME**__ than __**OTHERS**__.

> ## WHERE DO I GET MY VALUES:
> ### THE WORLD

> ## WHERE DO I GET MY VALUES:
> ### GOD'S WORD

2.) What is going to __**LAST THE LONGEST**__?

3.) Will I choose what's __**EASY**__ or what's __**BEST**__?

LIVING BY YOUR VALUES IS CALLED

__ALIGNMENT__

__INTEGRITY__

__CONGRUENCE__

4.) Is it worth __**THE PRICE**__?

SESSION 3: MAXIMIZING YOUR STRENGTHS

> ## GOD WAS:
> **INTIMATELY INVOLVED** IN MY BIRTH

1.) **DISCOVER** my SHAPE

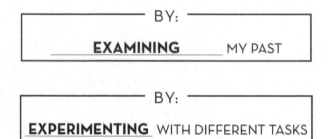

> ## BY:
> **EXAMINING** MY PAST

> ## BY:
> **EXPERIMENTING** WITH DIFFERENT TASKS

2.) **ACCEPT** my SHAPE

> ## BARRIERS TO FULFILLING MY SHAPE:
> **COMPARING** AND **CONFORMING**

> ## WHY MUST I MAXIMIZE MY SHAPE?
> BECAUSE I'M **ACCOUNTABLE** TO MY CREATOR

SESSION 4: LEARNING TO BE FAST AND SLOW

WHEN TO MOVE FAST:

1.) When God tells me __**TO DO SOMETHING**__ .

2.) When I need to ask or offer __**FORGIVENESS**__ .

3.) When I feel __**TEMPTED**__ .

4.) When I've made a __**PROMISE TO GOD**__ .

5.) When I have the opportunity __**TO DO GOOD**__ .

6.) When God offers me __**SALVATION**__ .

WHEN TO MOVE SLOW:

1.) When I don't have __**THE FACTS**__ .

2.) When I'm __**HURT**__ or __**ANGRY**__ .

3.) When making a __**MAJOR DECISION**__ .

4.) When waiting for a seed I've planted __**TO GROW**__ .

KEY VERSES

SESSION 1:

If the ax is dull and its edge unsharpened,
more strength is needed, but skill will bring success.
ECCLESIASTES 10:10 (NIV, EMPHASIS ADDED)

SESSION 2:

"Everything is permissible for me," but not everything is beneficial.
1 CORINTHIANS 6:12 (BSB)

SESSION 3:

Before I shaped you in the womb, I knew all about you.
Before you saw the light of day, I had holy plans for you.
JEREMIAH 1:5 (THE MESSAGE)

SESSION 4:

There is a right time and a right way to do everything,
but we know so little!
ECCLESIASTES 8:6 (GNT)

NOTES & PRAYERS

NOTES & PRAYERS

NOTES & PRAYERS

NOTES & PRAYERS

NOTES & PRAYERS

TOOLBOX FOR LIFE: FOUR SKILLS YOU NEED TO SUCCEED